Draw Your Way
to a **Younger Brain**

Also in the series:

Draw Your Way to a Younger Brain: Cats
Draw Your Way to a Younger Brain: Dogs

Also by the same author:

Colour Me Mindful: Birds
Colour Me Mindful: Butterflies
Colour Me Mindful: Enchanted Creatures
Colour Me Mindful: Seasons
Colour Me Mindful: Tropical
Colour Me Mindful: Underwater

Draw Your Way
to a **Younger Brain**
SAFARI

Anastasia Catris

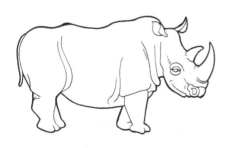

This edition first published in Great Britain in 2015
by Orion
an imprint of the Orion Publishing Group Ltd
Carmelite House
50 Victoria Embankment
London EC4Y 0DZ
An Hachette UK Company

1 3 5 7 9 10 8 6 4 2

A CIP catalogue record for this book
is available from the British Library.

ISBN: 978 1 4091 6548 4

Printed in Italy

The Orion Publishing Group's policy is to use papers
that are natural, renewable and recyclable and made
from wood grown in sustainable forests. The logging and
manufacturing processes are expected to conform to the
environmental regulations of the country of origin.

Every effort has been made to fulfil requirements with regard
to reproducing copyright material. The author and publisher will
be glad to rectify any omissions at the earliest opportunity.

www.orionbooks.co.uk

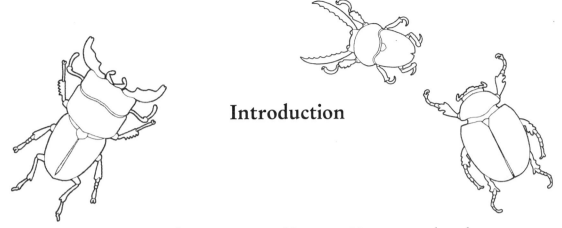

Introduction

It is never too late to try something new. Many researchers have shown that learning a new skill will develop your brain. Taking up and practicing a new set of skills, particularly combinations of abilities such as those involved in drawing – which blend looking, thinking and doing – will encourage brain development in several areas. In a recent project I was involved in at Newcastle University that was featured in a BBC documentary, we showed how taking up art produced improved cognitive performance after a few weeks of practice. Better still, there is now evidence that keeping up a wide range of regular activities and staying healthy can significantly reduce the chances of developing dementia.

The more you challenge your brain, the more you enhance your thinking, so taking up a new activity will do you good. When you start with drawing, it doesn't matter if you are good or bad; even Michelangelo had to learn once! The more you practice, the more you can maintain and improve your artistic abilities and brain function. As you progress through drawing, enjoy the art you are creating. Learning to be an artist can give you great pleasure, and it can help keep you well.

Daniel Collerton
Consultant Clinical Psychologist

About the author

After graduating from Royal Holloway, University of London with a BA Hons in English Literature, Anastasia Catris travelled to the United States to pursue her passion for illustration by studying at The Kubert School of Comic and Cartoon Art.

She returned to the UK in 2009, and has since worked as a freelance illustrator for HarperCollins, *Kerrang!*, Fox, Marvel, DC and *Cygnus Alpha: The Doctor Who Fanzine*. Ana lives in Wales, United Kingdom, and is an advocate of art therapy and of the health benefits of drawing.

www.anastasiacatris.com
Instagram: @AnastasiaCatris

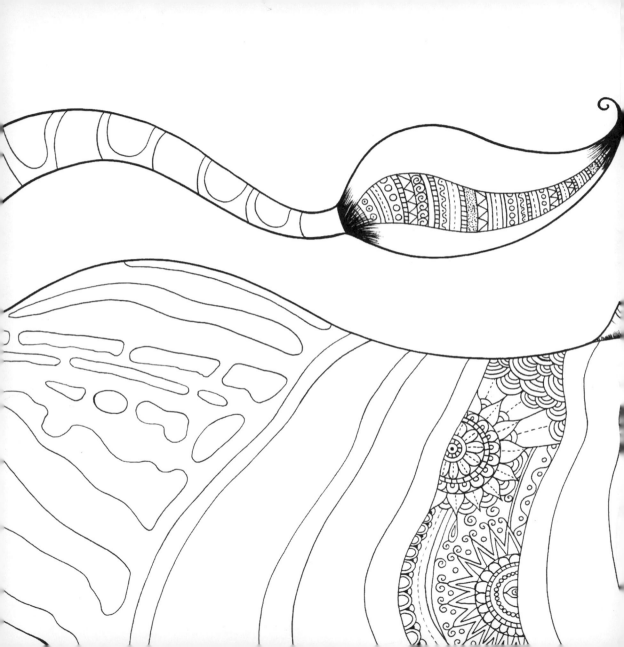

Fill the safari landscape

Draw your own safari inspired patterns

Fill this alligator with beautiful
scales and patterns

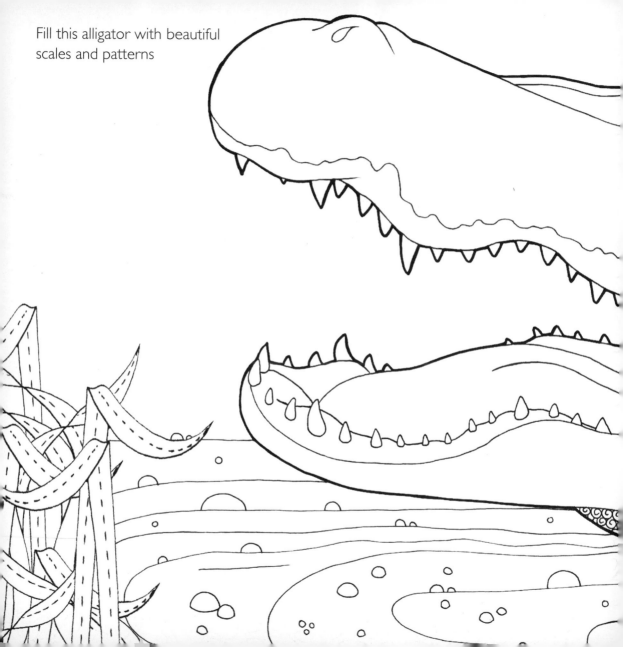

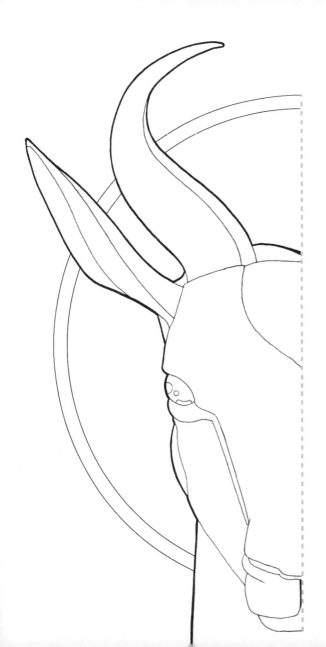

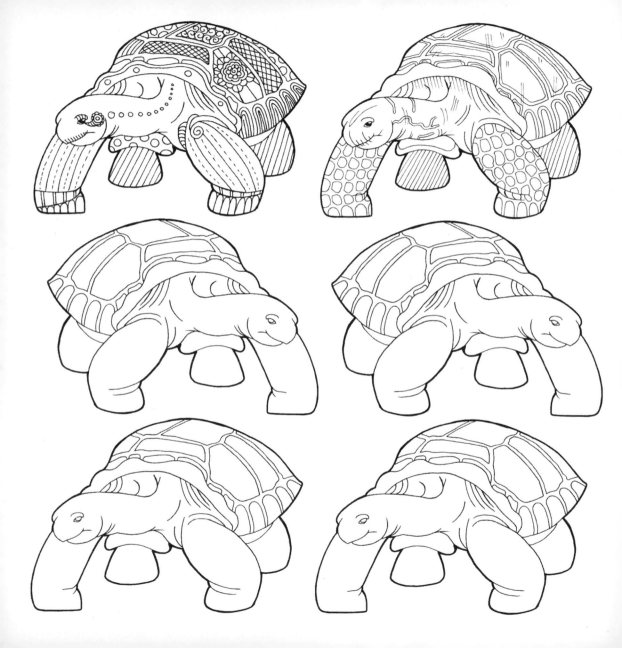

Surround this hippopotamus with colourful fish

Decorate this water buffalo's large horns

Draw these pretty
flamingos' reflections

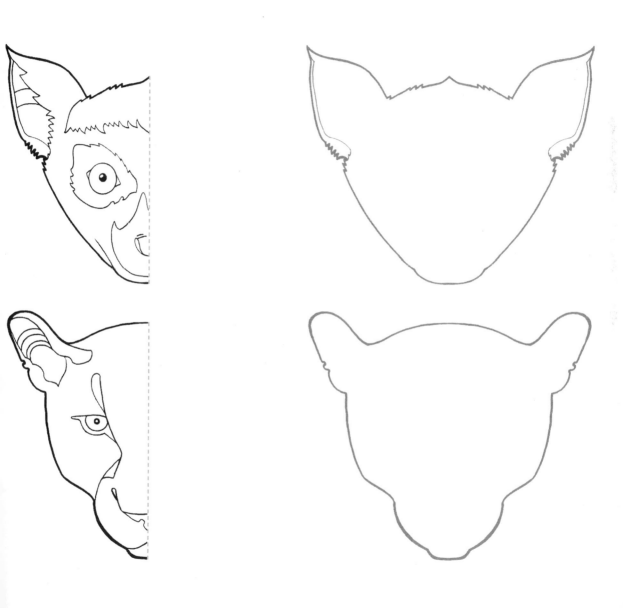

What do you see in your binoculars?

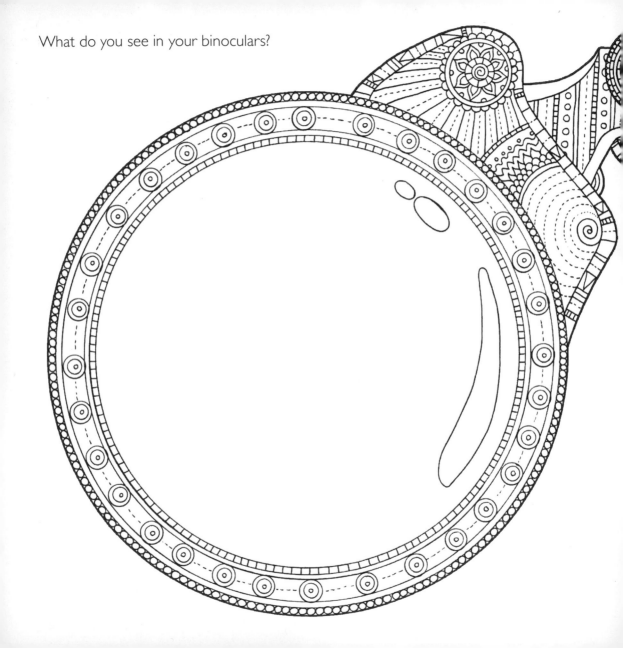

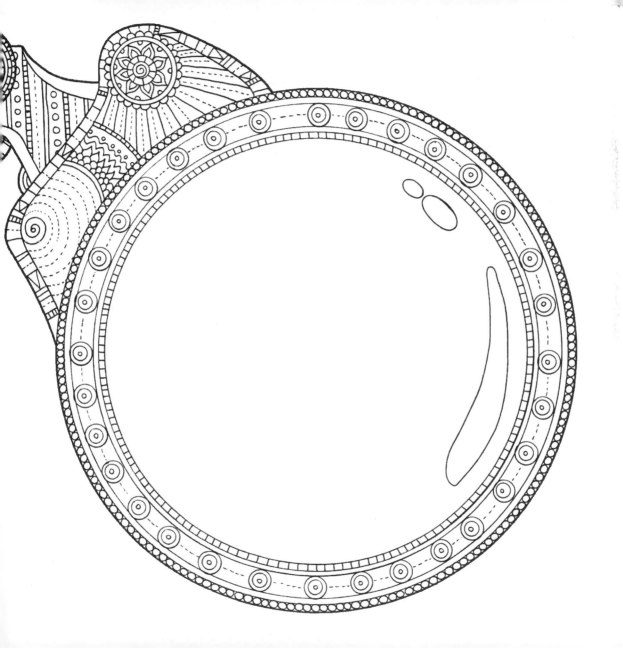

Fill the night sky with bats and stars

Dress these two adventurers ready for their safari

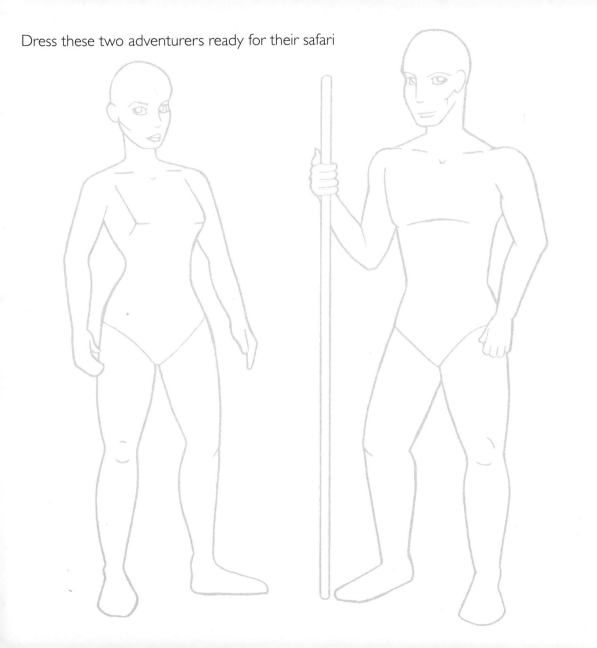

What is chasing these antelope?

Collect all the books in the
DRAW YOUR WAY TO A YOUNGER BRAIN
series

DRAW YOUR WAY TO A YOUNGER BRAIN

CATS

AN ART THERAPY BOOK

Anastasia Catris

DRAW YOUR WAY TO A YOUNGER BRAIN

DOGS

AN ART THERAPY BOOK

Anastasia Catris

DRAW YOUR WAY TO A YOUNGER BRAIN

SAFARI

AN ART THERAPY BOOK

Anastasia Catris